Raise the Bar
Grades 6-8

Drum Kit

Teaching Notes written by James Sedge & Chris Walters

Published by
Trinity College London Press Ltd
trinitycollege.com

Registered in England
Company no. 09726123

Printed in England by Caligraving Ltd

Contents

  * demo track available to download
** demo & backing track available to download
See inside back cover for details.

Drum Kit Legend

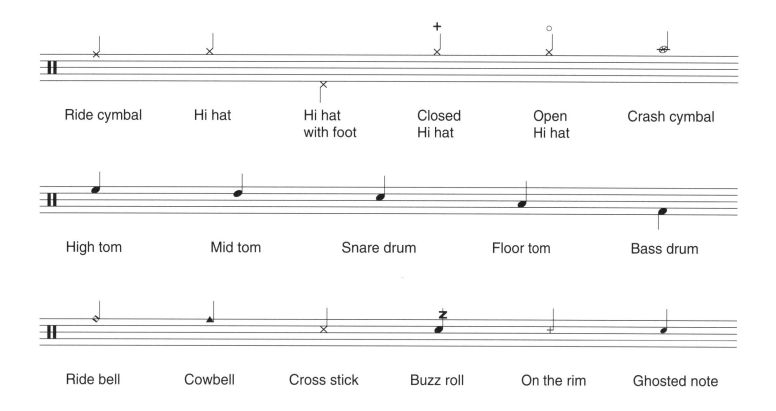

| Ride cymbal | Hi hat | Hi hat with foot | Closed Hi hat | Open Hi hat | Crash cymbal |

| High tom | Mid tom | Snare drum | Floor tom | Bass drum |

| Ride bell | Cowbell | Cross stick | Buzz roll | On the rim | Ghosted note |

Please note that the notation used for ride cymbal (and bell), crash cymbal and cross stick has changed from that used in previous Trinity College London publications. Drum kit notation varies between different publishers/ arrangers but the key above is becoming more consistently used.

Teaching Notes – Grade 6

1. Hava Banhava (Malcolm Ball)

This piece explores Eastern European Klezmer-influenced music and a Middle Eastern sound in the context of a contemporary groove. The tempo is the same throughout, although the pulse changes from minim to crotchet at bar 27, and back to minim at bar 44. Look carefully at the rhythm from bar 28, where a syncopated groove begins. The 'z' articulation in bar 69 indicates a buzzed roll on the snare drum.

2. Mongo's Rug (Paul Clarvis)

This piece uses hands, sticks and mallets. You'll need to be adept at changing between these, ensuring that the rhythms come through clearly and precisely throughout. When playing with your hands, use open or slap strokes according to your taste. The *gliss.* effect can be made by wetting the third finger, supporting it with the thumb and sliding it across the surface of the head, possibly after you have struck the head with the other hand.

3. Salema (Paul Francis)

Use soft mallets on the crash cymbal at the start of this piece. At bar 3 there is a cross-over pattern on the toms and snare (with the snares off) before the piece moves into an Afro-Cuban section at bar 15 (with the snares on). You've got three bars to change from mallets to sticks just before this. Be sure to keep the hi hat going throughout the solo at bars 27-34. Enjoy the reggae section at bar 39, and be precise with the semiquaver sextuplets at bar 52 – you might find that a sticking pattern of RLRLRR, LRLRLL works well here. Study clave patterns to prepare yourself for the section at bar 57.

4. Sumo Song (Troy Miller)

There are seven beats per bar in this piece, which poses a considerable counting challenge – although you should find that the backing track will help you stay on course. Keep the opening groove stable by leaning into the pedalled hi hat, a technique that might also help you in the eight-bar solo later on. Remember that timekeeping is paramount in the solo, so don't allow your creativity to distract you from the pulse. The coda section is this piece's 'sting in the tail', so be sure to save enough concentration to ensure that the rhythm is tight and accurate here.

5. Iron Horse (Pete Riley & Andy Staples)

This piece is based on the 'gallop' feel typical of Iron Maiden. At figure A, and also later at E, be sure to base your fills around the notated hits. This gives you a chance to perform your own ideas around a set of defined accents. Nicko McBrain, the drummer of Iron Maiden, uses a single bass drum pedal, even for rapid repeated semiquavers like at figure B, so try to do the same for an authentic sound. Use the triplet crotchets, a bar before figure D, as a springboard into the shuffle feel.

6. Three's a Crowd (Stevie Smith)

Here is a study in different types of three time with some challenging transitions between sections. First comes a section with polyrhythmic motifs, calling for accurate placement of accents. This is followed by an Afro-Cuban groove which requires a light feel. A jazz waltz section eventually leads to a prog-rock section at figure E. You'll need to slot quickly into each new groove to make these stylistic shifts work. The $\frac{3}{8}$ at bar 56 feels counter-intuitive, so count this carefully!

1. Hava Banhava

Malcolm Ball

Play with dynamics appropriate to the music

Grade 6

6   = a left stick buzzed roll on SD

2. Mongo's Rug

Paul Clarvis

* Rapid movement of the fingers 4321.

** *gliss.* is produced by finger friction on the drum head.

8

3. Salema

Paul Francis

4. Sumo Song

Troy Miller

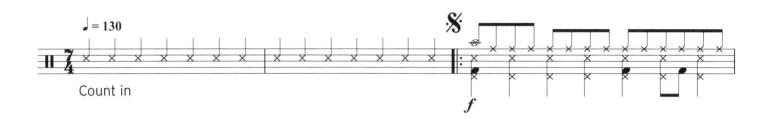

Count in

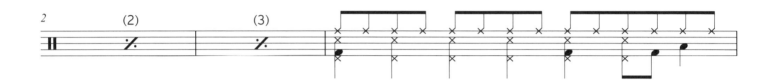

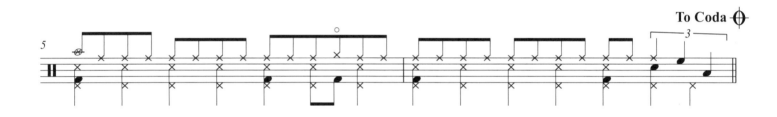

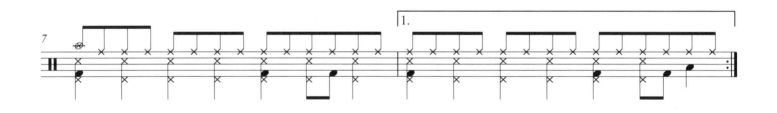

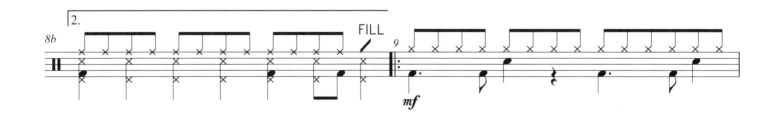

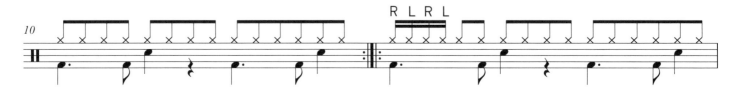

5. Iron Horse

Pete Riley/Andy Staples

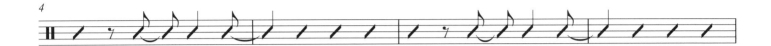

= performer's choice of drum(s) to be played using rhythm shown.
Play with dynamics appropriate to the music

14

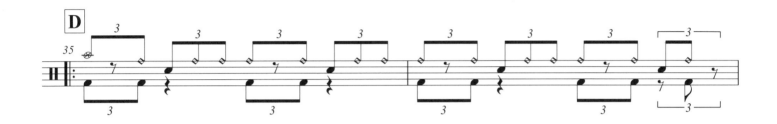

Grade 6

6. Three's a Crowd

Stevie Smith

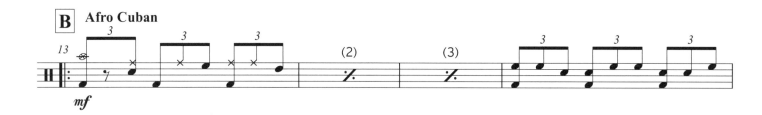

16

Teaching Notes – Grade 7

7. Present and Correct (Andrew Tween)

This piece is inspired by Steve Gadd, and many of his licks can be found within it, including from 'Crazy Army' and '50 Ways to Leave Your Lover'. It is also a study of linear style – this is when you only play one sound source at a time. One challenging aspect of this is that you cannot rely on the hi hat for timing, so you'll have to keep your sense of pulse strong. Look out for the inward paradiddle between the snare and cowbell at bar 34 and the orchestrated six-stroke roll idea at bar 39.

8. Lazybones (George Double)

A lazy, half-swung groove is the foundation for this piece. From bar 13, splash the pedal hi hat with your foot, experimenting with the distance between the hi hat cymbals – between half a centimetre and a centimetre will probably give you the best sound. A study of shuffles (or half swing) would be beneficial for this song, as the bottom half of the kit is shuffled, including the bass drum.
As ever, keep time in the solo, resisting the urge to sacrifice pulse for creative invention.

9. Blakesley Avenue (Rick Hudson & Alan Barnes)

This piece follows a fairly traditional jazz-standard format, and the Latin groove used from bar 9 is a rhythm that Art Blakey featured on many of his recordings. Use the shoulder of the stick on the bell of the cymbal to get a clear articulation, and note where you are instructed to switch from Latin to swing and vice versa. You'll need convincing comping skills from bar 39 – it's authentic that there is nothing in the notation here. Listen to the piano in the backing track to get an idea of the feel.

10. Traveller (Troy Miller)

This demanding piece contains many subtleties and ambiguities. Listen carefully to the click on the backing track – it really helps! It might also help you to think of a $\frac{4}{4}$ triplet feel – although there is still much complexity to navigate within this conception of the groove. Make sure that you don't obscure the piano during your improvisation at bar 37, but improvise freely nevertheless.

11. Off Limits (Neil Robinson)

A study of ghost notes and clean controlled hi hat playing is the focus here. There should be a clear distinction between the ghosted and accented notes on the snare. Perhaps use the left hand for the open hi hats in bars 28-30 so that the ride and the hi hat can be played together. As well as executing the various technical demands, try to achieve a solid funky feel throughout.

12. For Art's Sake (Stevie Smith)

There should be a strong funk feel throughout this piece, which requires considerable stamina due to its somewhat relentless nature. Try to keep the ghost notes clean to emphasise the shifting accent patterns, and keep the semiquavers rhythmically even throughout. The hits at figure E can be orchestrated however you wish. Note that the pattern at bar 72 is played by clicking the sticks together over the bass drum, and be sure to observe the long crescendo here.

7. Present and Correct

Andrew Tween

The slash through the note stem indicates double strokes.

8. Lazybones

George Double

* HH splash with foot.

22 Play with dynamics appropriate to the music.

9. Blakesley Avenue

Rick Hudson/Alan Barnes

10. Traveller

Troy Miller

11. Off Limits

Neil Robinson

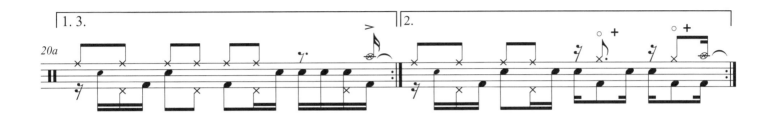

D.C. al Coda

Coda

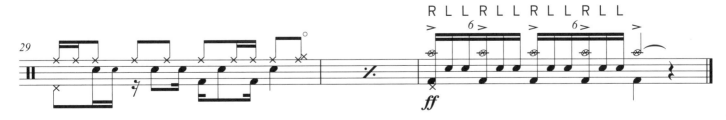

12. For Art's Sake

Stevie Smith

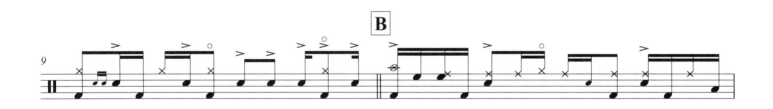

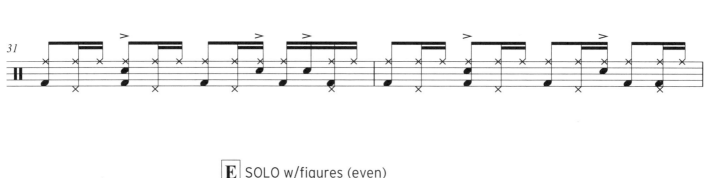

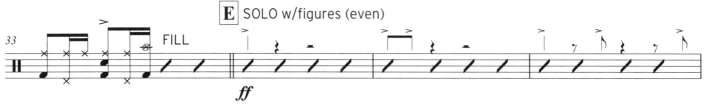

Teaching Notes – Grade 8

13. Lindsay's Umbrella Dance (Paul Clarvis)

There are various notational and rhythmic challenges to overcome in this piece, first of all in the opening section. Here, **colla voce** suggests that you should follow and respond to the melody in the backing track, adding complementary sounds and colours freely on the drum kit. From figure A onwards it might be an idea to memorise the melody and its shapes, which are indicated on the ossia stave. Whether or not you learn the melody, you'll need to internalise the different feels of $\frac{5}{16}$ and $\frac{7}{16}$ and manage the transitions between them efficiently.

14. Swiss Swagger (Troy Miller)

This piece is a triplet-based exercise which will help develop your left hand if you follow the suggested sticking pattern in bar 9. Focus on your feet from bar 7 onwards to help root the groove. Also in bar 7, make sure that the flams are clearly audible, and note that there are two bars of this pattern, which should sound identical. The shift back to semiquavers at bar 16 should be tight, with careful attention paid to the considerable amount of detail in the rest of the piece.

15. 7evens (Pete Riley)

There is rhythmic trickery going on in the opening bar of this piece, which implies two bars of $\frac{7}{16}$ plus two extra semiquavers. You'll need to count this carefully in order to land confidently on beat 1 of the next bar. At bar 4 you switch to $\frac{7}{8}$ and stay in this time signature for the rest of the piece. There are two-bar patterns throughout, a result of the odd number of quavers in each bar. An example, among many, is the shifting of the open-and-closed hi hat pattern in relation to the bar in the section starting at bar 40. This and all similar two-bar patterns will require careful counting.

16. Overture (Ralph Salmins)

This piece requires you to be proficient at a number of different styles as well as the transitions between them. An overture is usually played at the start of a musical theatre production and is a preview of the music that will be played during the show. The drummer plays an important role, 'conducting' the band and helping them snap into each groove quickly and effectively. This means that you'll need to glide effortlessly between styles while inhabiting them all convincingly. Make the fill in bars 158-159 as showy as possible!

17. Super High Five (Mark Schulman)

A study of samba playing would be helpful for this piece. The accents really need to poke through, so all unaccented notes should be played relatively quietly. You'll need to be able to play clean double strokes with accents included, for example in bar 39. At bar 51, the $\frac{10}{16}$ time signature is essentially two groups of five semiquavers, which feels like a compression of the pulse after $\frac{5}{4}$. Count carefully to keep up here, and hold the pulse steady as you crescendo to $\boldsymbol{ff}$.

18. Purple Pumpkin (Luke Wastell)

This entertaining piece requires you to play a tambourine with your right hand and read two staves, one for each hand, while doing so. Other tricky features include the three-note buzz rolls at figure A; having just two beats to change from tambourine to stick in bar 37; and a solo at bars 53-56 which should keep the feel of the groove going while adding an extra layer of variety.

13. Lindsay's Umbrella Dance

Paul Clarvis

*The drum sounds chosen should be appropriate to the style of the music.

*The **Fine** is at the start of the third semiquaver of bar 53. The notes in brackets are not played on the D.S.

SOLOS

After solos, D.S. al Fine

x8

p crescendo throughout, following soloist

14. Swiss Swagger

Troy Miller

15. 7evens

Pete Riley

16. Overture

Ralph Salmins

= performer's choice of drum(s) to be played using rhythm shown.

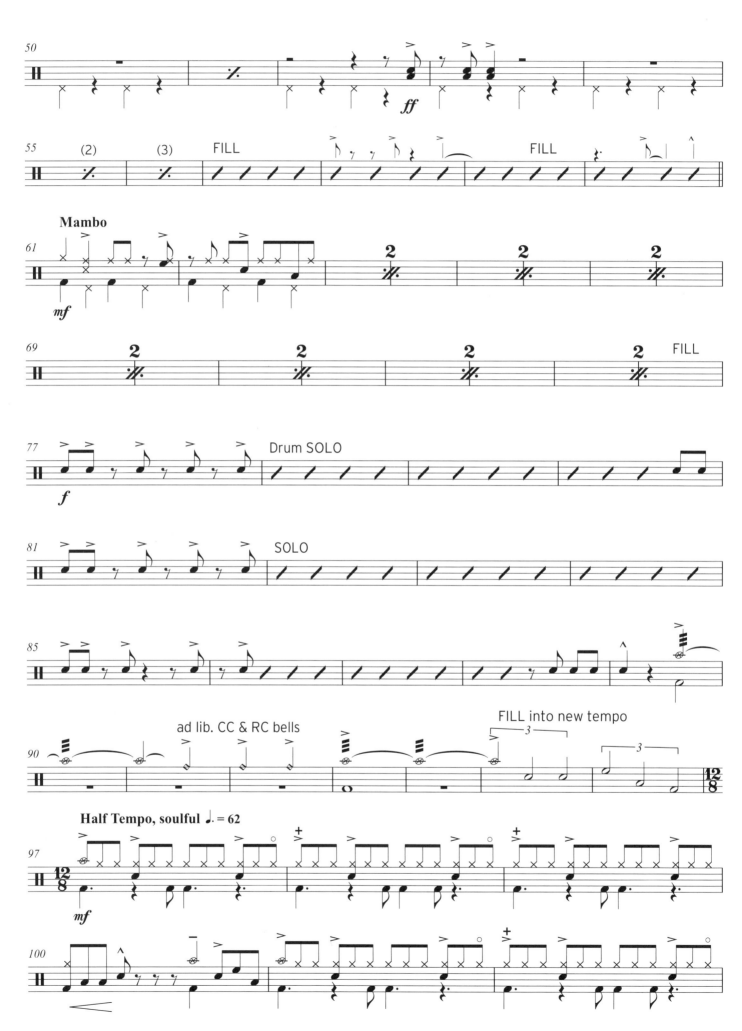

17. Super High Five

Mark Schulman

* = Two Crash cymbals

18. Purple Pumpkin

Luke Wastell

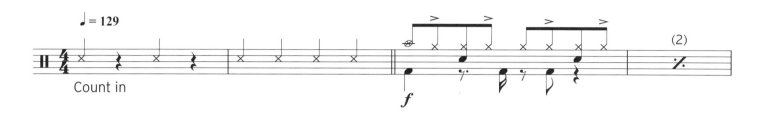

Count in

take Tambourine

B Right hand
Tamb.

Left hand

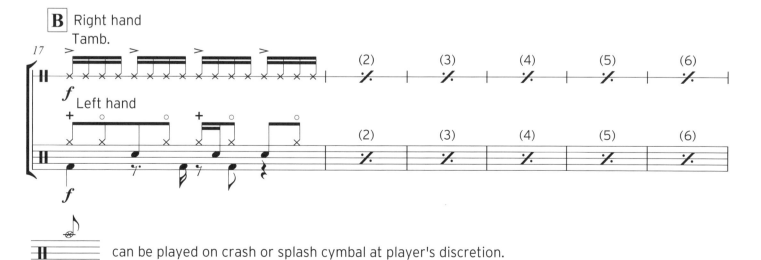

can be played on crash or splash cymbal at player's discretion.

The Cowbell should be mounted/attached to the kit in a place convenient to the player.

49

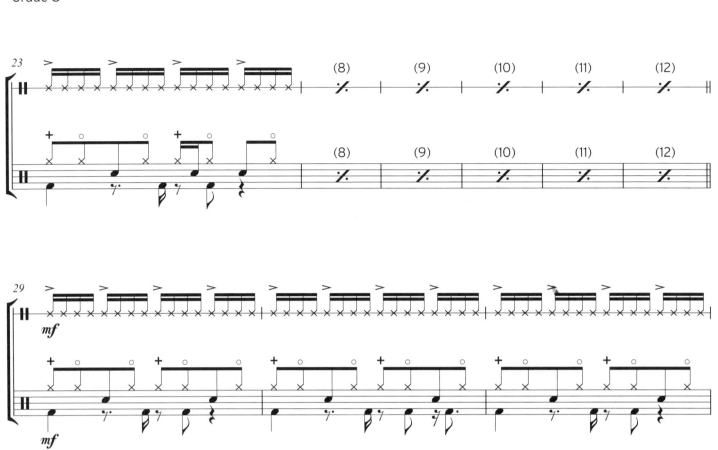

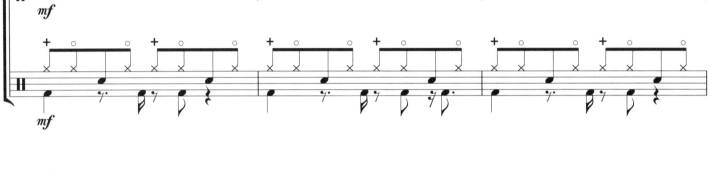

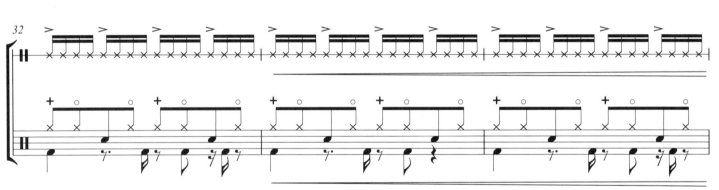

Tamb. down,
take stick

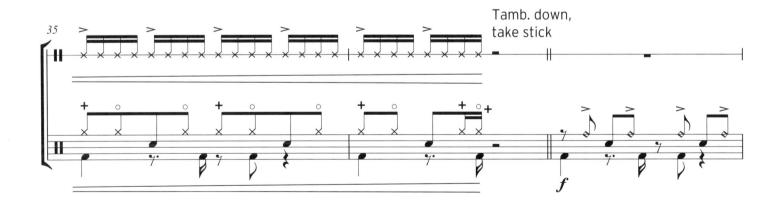